First published as a hardback in 2018 by One Makes a Difference Publishing

ISBN 978-1-9999694-0-0

Text copyright © Glyn Ivor 2018
www.glynivor.com

Illustrations copyright © Zoe Sadler 2018
www.zoesadler.com

Printed and bound in the UK

Designed by Inkyeverafter Press

One Makes a Difference

Glyn
Ivor

Illustrated by

Zoe
Sadler

Dev's for her untiring support

Dad 'Ivor' – unfulfilled dreams
Mum

Atchoo!

There's a house in a street, in a town near Somewhere,
Where the lorries and cars always foggle the air.
Young Izzy lives here, at the top of The Hill,
Living close to the road, often makes her quite ill.

Poor Izzy coughs and puffs and sniffs and wheezes,
With cough number ten, come whopping great sneezes!
So mum phones 999 for Paramedic Steve,
On arriving he finds Izzy struggling to breathe.

In the ambulance, Mum says, 'You'll be fine.'
Siren and blue lights, they ignore a STOP sign.
The hospital's a long way, Steve drives super-fast,
Through green and red lights, they get there at last.

A doctor takes one look. 'Pollution! I'm sure.
Fresh air's the solution, the start of a cure.
Be beside the sea and find yourself some sun.'
'I know just the place!' cries Izzy's lovely mum.

'Uncle John lives on an island surrounded by sea,
In a white painted lighthouse high on a quay.
Uncle John's been a fisherman all of his life,
Scamp's his dog and Aunty Barbara's his wife.'

The Isle of Wight is brilliant and a great place to stay,
I've been here two weeks and feel better each day.

See I can twirl, I can spin, and I can whirl until I'm dizzy.
Oops, sorry! How rude not to say 'Hi, I'm Izzy!
Actually, my name is Isobel, but I'm called Izzy for short.
I can't believe how I feel – I'm usually too ill for sport.'

'By the way now I'm getting to know you quite well…
Please keep a secret. Say promise. I've something to tell.
It happened last week, when I was down on the beach,
By some rocks, in the sea and just out of reach.

I thought, is it a box, or a barrel, a crate or a case?
Then I glimpsed purple hair, two hands – and her face!
She gargled and gurgled, with gravelly grit squeaks,
Splibbered and splobbered then kind of like, speaks.'

'I'm trapped by a net! It's wrapped round my tail.'
She looked sort of strange, with a face sort of pale.
How silly! Trapped by her tail. She sank and was gone.
I shouted 'Don't worry! I'll hurry to find Uncle John.'

He was mending a net, on the seat of his boat,
I cried – 'Quickly! Hurry!' – Soon we were afloat.
Uncle John's dead strong. He can row really fast.
I pointed to the rocks and we got there at last.

We pulled and we heaved! Uncle John cut the net.
There was a thrashing and splashing, we got very wet!
Then Uncle John gave a laugh from deep in his belly.
So that he wibbled and wobbled and shook like a jelly.

As he laughed at me he said: 'Izzy–you're silly…
I'm soaked to the skin and now feel very chilly.
A humpy back whale or a purply ling made the splash,
Or a dogfish, or a codfish, or a prickly finned bass.'

'It was a squid. No an octopus. I could tell by the feel.
No! A pollock or haddock, more likely a slippery old eel!'
I looked at him and smiled. I knew what I'd seen.
Dogfish and codfish don't have tails that are green!

At home by the fire aunty dried us both off.
Saying 'hot honey and lemon will fight off a cough.'

Out of my round window, there are no lorries or cars,
I hear waves crashing below, and see thousands of stars.
I love this lighthouse, perched high on the quay,
But what I love most of all is—a mermaid has spoken to me.

New Friends

I've sat on the sand for seven days – or perhaps eight?
Wondering how much longer must I sit here and wait?
But just when I think it's time to get up and play,
The hands on my watch start to turn the wrong way.

Wow! Look at the sea sparkle with rainbows of light!
Their colours dazzle my eyes and blur my sight.
There are huge waves and a rushing noise in the air.
Now calm – with a mermaid – bob bobbing – with long purple hair.

She looks straight at me but says nothing,
Staring at each other, we both start laughing.
She has a squeaky laugh, like a strange giggle,
So that right down to her tail she starts to wiggle.

'My name is Laguna I'm not from round here,
I must look very strange, but there's nothing to fear.
I've seen you waiting, mermaids don't usually speak,
But I had to thank you, for how you saved me last week.'

'We swim just like fishes, yet no matter how we try,
We must surface for air, otherwise we would die.
Being trapped under water is very dangerous for me,
Izzy, I owe you my life — thank you for cutting me free.'

She's just called me Izzy! I haven't told her my name.
'It's alright,' she says quickly, 'I can explain…
Mermaids speak using thoughts when we're under the sea,
So to know all about you Izzy, is very easy for me.'

I smile – 'I know you're a mermaid, I will not pretend,
But all I want is… to have a very best friend!'
We talked and we swam, and we played all day long,
Woof! A dog barked – flipping her tail she was gone.

The Unicorns Message

Today Laguna said… 'Mermaids really don't understand,
Why people still pollute the air, our sea and their land?
You know, it's not only humans, pollution makes poorly.
Lie back… Close your eyes… Let me tell you a story.'
Laguna whispy sings, in a very strange sort of way,
So that Izzy feels like she's floating… floating… floating away!

'Laguna, Laguna, Laguna, Lagoo,
A rhyming tale I'm singing to you.
Is it pretend and just a rhyme
Is it about today, or far back in time?
Is it made up, or could it be true,
Is it about someone else, or all about you?
The answer is easy, it's not hard to find,
Listen to Laguna, and make up your mind.
Laguna, Laguna, Laguna, Lagoo,
Listen to this song I'm singing to you.'

When the earth was young and the air was still clean,
Unicorns were the gentlest creatures you ever have seen.
Now the world lived happily for a very long time,
All living things were content, they were doing just fine.

But more humans were born year upon year,
To make extra room the forest they needed to clear.
Chopping down trees – building their houses of wood,
Then ploughing up that land, just as fast as they could.

Houses they built, first in ones – then in dozens,
For their brothers and sisters and aunties and cousins.
People needed more food, their animals more hay,
So they had to keep chopping – yes day after day.

Chopping and building – with nothing to fear,
Burning and ploughing – year upon year.
As the years passed, extra space was found,
By more and more trees, being felled to the ground.

Now, nobody can remember the year or the day,
When the unicorns entered the village to say:
'You have to stop chopping – no more should you chop,
We've come here today to ask you to stop.'

'We speak for the forest – the woods and the trees,
For birds and butterflies also humble bumble bees.'

'We ask for the fishes – and all strange creatures with fins,
Also seals and turtles – in fact everything that swims.'

'For ugly blobs wiggling in green ditches and bogs,
And the newts, pollywiggles, the slimies and frogs.'

'We speak for the innocents – all life without tongues,
Also large animals and small animals, even very tiny ones.'

'We ask for the tree fairies – as well as the elves,
For all living things, that can't speak for themselves.'

'We beg for bright coloured creatures and dull ones too,
Brown or grey mottled and dazzling orange or blue.'

'All animals in cages that you keep in the zoo,
If you don't heed our warnings – things will soon affect you!'

'Every one of us needs clean water, land and air
But you're chopping and burning as if you haven't a care.
The air you are smogging, with smoke black and thick,
Which we're forced to breathe in and it's making us sick.'

'From the land you are growing crop after crop,
By spreading it all with your slipperty-slop.
This causes foul smelling goo, to seep through the ground,
Polluting our streams, so clean water cannot be found.
The rivers are smelling and just about keep flowing,
But very slowly, down to the sea the whole lot is going.'

The headman replied:
'Unicorns we hear you, we've been listening well,
But in answer to you, we've something to tell.
We have mothers, wives and many children to feed,
And it's warnings like this, we don't really need.'

'With the wood we build houses and logs keep us warm,
We grow crops on OUR land, so we're doing no harm.
As long as the goo, from our fields keeps flowing,
To be frank, we don't really care where it's all going.'

'We can see that you're worried, that's quite clear,
But let's reassure you, we have nothing to fear.
In fact we can continue, like this, year upon year,
Yes year upon year, with nothing to fear!'

But the men didn't know the damage they caused,
When they chopped down one tree,
And that one had to be multiplied by ten thousand,
                              two hundred and three.

The unicorn's heads drooped, they had no more to say,
It was the last time men saw them – right down to today.
As they left the village, there fell a single gold tear,
While the men shouted: 'we all have nothing to fear!'

But that wasn't true, for the wise unicorns understood,
The problems were more, than just the chopping of wood.
The land had begun to turn, from bright green to dull grey,
And although unicorns never die, they would start fading away.

Up mountains and down valleys, they travelled the land,
Coming to a great ocean – edged with soft yellow sand.
Taking a last look behind, they walked into the sea.
Yet they left something behind for you and for me.

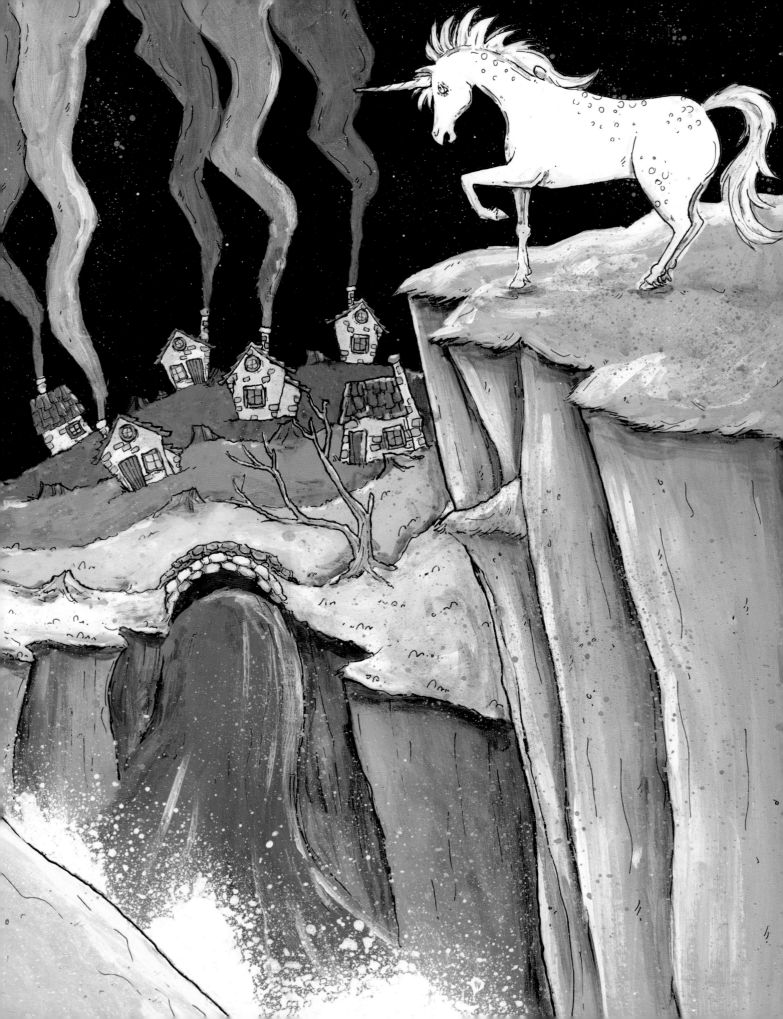

A great rolling wave, edged with green, blue and gold.
Which grew larger, as it came nearer, just before it rolled.
I could see right inside – through the foam and the spray,
Silver unicorns – yes I saw them – how many? I can't say.

Their wet manes glistened, like rainbows they shone,
As the wave rumbled and tumbled and fell – they were gone!
Laguna opened her hand – inside was a single gold tear,
'Izzy I give it to you, the reason one day, will be clear.'

I awoke, with the sun on my face and my head on the sand,
With the tide around my feet, and a gold tear in my hand.
Laguna had vanished, so I turned away from the sea,
My tummy was rumbling, I knew, I was late for my tea.

'Hi, remember me? I've grown, but, I'm still called Izzy,
Since I spoke to you last, I've been really quite busy.
I work on the Isle of Wight, near Uncle John,
He still laughs and says, 'Izzy you surely were wrong!'

He says he touched a squid, he could tell by the feel
And mermaids are pretend, it's only squid that are real.
So, was it just a story, or are there parts that are true,
Here's the golden tear, a secret I'm sharing with you.

I was only nine years old – which was still quite young,
When Laguna whispered, what needs to be done.
So I worked hard at school and at college too,
What Laguna shared with me, I'll now share with you.

The golden tear is full of HOPE—something quite real,
Young people have HOPE and it changes how we feel.
It can be very small, but still affect our hearts and minds,
As Laguna said… 'The answers are not too hard to find.'

We must look after our earth before it's too late,
Starting today, as there's no time to wait.
We can't continue to pollute the land, air and sea,
Or Earth will continue to die—for you and for me.

When the unicorns warned men, it was a long time ago,
Yet the world's population continues to grow.
We're still chopping down trees and building and burning,
After all of this time, it doesn't appear that we're learning.

More animals in our forests become extinct every day,
And from mens minds, unicorns have almost faded away.
We need to help them, before they fade for good,
It may take lots off effort, but I still think that we should.

So it's up to us all, to change some of the things that we do,
What? Well the unicorns and Laguna gave us a clue.
We must look after our earth — it's the only one we've got,
And that...

One Makes a Difference, Because One Becomes a Lot.

So next time think!

When you drop your rubbish on the street or the floor,
(If we all did the same)
There could be another ten million, two hundred and four.

If you leave lights on all day and waste energy,
(If we all did the same)
Think how much is wasted, multiplied by two billion and three.

If you walk where you're heading instead of going by car,
It probably won't kill you because it's usually not far…
Instead of creating clouds of grey fogulous smoke,
The air would be cleaner; we'd have no reason to choke!

When you waste your food like, pasta, pizza or pie,
(If we all did the same)
It could create a pile right up to the sky.

When you pick wild flowers to put in a vase,
(If we all did the same)
The massive great total would be more than the stars.

If you throw things away, just to buy a new one,
(If we all did the same)
The pile of junk would stretch all the way to the sun.

When you leave a tap on so it runs in the sink,
(If we all did the same)
The wasted water would leave none left to drink.
So turn that tap off, what a little time it takes,
And save water equal to over 500 large lakes!

If you think about it, the reverse can be true,
To help the environment there's many things you can do.

If you planted one tree, and I'm sure that you could,
(If we all did the same)
The result would equal a 1000-hectare wood.
Think of the all the animals that could live there,
So planting a tree each would show that we care.

If you recycle your bottles, cans, paper and foil,
(If we all did the same)
None would have to be buried deep under the soil.

Help dig a pond, what a short time it takes!
(If we all did the same)
Together they would be bigger than hundreds of lakes.
All the toads, frogs and newts, would then have a home,
No more dirty ditches would they have to roam.

You see there are so many things that we can all do.
I know there's much more, but I'll leave them to you.

By working together, the earth will be clean enough one day,
Possibly for unicorns to gallop from the salty waves and spray.
They could run on green grass, through their forests and wood,
Breathing in pure clean air, just as you and I should.

So finally, the moral of this story, in case you've forgot,
Is that…

One Makes a Difference, Because One Becomes a Lot.

Do mermaids really exist? Well if you're still in doubt,
Visit The Isle of Wight and perhaps you'll find out!

CHARLOTTE'S

ZOO

Thanks & Things

Especially to Zoe, for her inspirational illustrations
that animate my words so wonderfully. www.zoesadler.com

Karen Ball for rounding off some corners! karen@speckledpen.com

Caroline, Theodora, Edd, Laura, Taz, Monique (Peanut) & Sebastian.

Rod and Susan for their many years of unconditional friendship and love.

Emma, Rich, George and Erica.

Joni, Iain, Sophie and Ewan.

Jaqueline & Emily for initial thoughts and suggestions.

The good (and not so good) people of Appledore in North Devon, especially:
In my memory – John, Barbara & Scamp.
Irsha Street (whom I miss terribly).
Ali & Graham and all the staff of the Beaver Inn where much of this tale was outlined.

The fine people of Laguna Beach, Southern California – where a seed was sown.

To the influences in my young life – whom I unashamedly try to emulate.

Alfred 'Fred' Bestall 1892-1986 writer and illustrator of Rupert Bear 1935-1965.
Those magical Rupert the Bear Annuals that captured my young imagination and heart…
Before life became complicated! I still can't do Origami!

Dr Seuss – Theodor Seuss Geisel 1904-1991
political cartoonist, poet, animator and book publisher.

Edward Lear 1812-1888 artist, illustrator, musician, author and poet.

Sir John Betjeman 1906-1984 poet laureate, writer and broadcaster.

£1 from each book sold will be donated to environmental charities
working on the Isle of Wight or used to plant trees on the Island.

Please send all your environmental suggestions to Izzy on the Isle of Wight
and she will try to respond as best she can – please be patient as she is very busy!

Izzy@glynivor.com   www.glynivor.com